new woman
jazz collection

D0353172

Published by
Wise Publications
8/9 Frith Street, London, W1D 3JB, England.

Exclusive Distributors:
Music Sales Limited
Distribution Centre, Newmarket Road,
Bury St Edmunds, Suffolk, IP33 3YB, England.
Music Sales Pty Limited
120 Rothschild Avenue, Rosebery, NSW 2018, Australia.

Order No. AM979374
ISBN 1-84449-378-4
This book © Copyright 2004 by Wise Publications.

Music arranged by Paul Honey & Derek Jones.
Music Engraved by Paul Ewers Music Design.
Music Edited by Lucy Holliday.
Compiled by Nick Crispin.
Cover photographs courtesy of LFI.

Your Guarantee of Quality:

As publishers, we strive to produce every book
to the highest commercial standards.

The book has been carefully designed to
minimise awkward page turns and to make
playing from it a real pleasure.

Particular care has been given to specifying
acid-free, neutral-sized paper made from pulps which
have not been elemental chlorine bleached.

This pulp is from farmed sustainable forests and
was produced with special regard for the environment.

Throughout, the printing and binding have been
planned to ensure a sturdy, attractive publication
which should give years of enjoyment.

If your copy fails to meet our high standards,
please inform us and we will gladly replace it.

Printed in Malta by Interprint Limited.

www.musicsales.com

ask a woman who knows natalie cole 2

be here to love me norah jones 20

be still my heart silje nergaard 8

blame it on the moon katie melua 16

call me lea delaria 32

call off the search katie melua 66

calling you holly cole 42

comes love stacey kent 23

compared to what roberta flack 50

crickets sing for anamaria astrud gilberto 62

dream of life carmen mcrae 72

east of the sun (and west of the moon) diana krall 78

fever peggy lee 69

fine and mellow billie holiday 82

help yourself amy winehouse 88

i wish i knew how it would feel to be free nina simone 100

it's oh so quiet lisa ekdahl 93

love has no pride jane monheit 124

the nearness of you norah jones 106

so nice (summer samba) bebel gilberto 110

that ole devil called love alison moyet 114

time is a healer eva cassidy 118

Wise Publications
part of The Music Sales Group
London / New York / Paris / Sydney /
Copenhagen / Berlin / Madrid / Tokyo

ask a woman who knows

Words & Music by Victor Abrams

just ask a wo-man who knows. We used to share our troub-les

and the good times___ too, now I'm left with all the woes.___

I'm not the on - ly___ sor - ry one, just ask a wo - man

who knows. The days are long, oh but the nights are long - er,

just ask the wo-man____ who knows._

When my on-ly con-so-la-tion is that I've got no-thing more_

be still my heart

Words & Music by Silje Nergaard & Mike McGurk

heart,_____ my heart be still.

Flugelhorn solo

1.

2.

Be-ware,_____ be still____ my heart,____ take care__ be still_____ my__ heart.__

blame it on the moon

Words & Music by Mike Batt

soon.
-ly.

I was fine,
Guil - ty feel -ings

feel - ing strong,
in the night,

did - n't want to fall in love_____
as I won - der is it wrong_____

_____ with a - ny - one.
_____ to feel so right?

Now that it's gone too far to call for a halt I'll

blame it on the moon 'cause it's not my fault.____

I did - n't think that this would hap - pen so soon

so I'll blame it on the moon.

19

be here to love me

Words & Music by Townes Van Zandt

1. Yeah, I see con-clu-sion in all this con-fu-sion of mine.
2. Chil-dren are dan-cing the gamb-ers are chan-cing their all.
3. World's come and gone, but a few stars hang on to the sky.

Though you and I both know it's on-ly the warm glow of wine that's
Win-dows ac-cus-ing the door of a-bus-ing the wall. But who
Well the wind's run-ning free but it ain't up to me to ask why. But the

got you to feel - ing this way.
cares what the night - watch - men say?
po - ets are de - mand - ing their pay

But I don't care, I want you to
The stage has been set for the
and they've left me with no - thing to

stay.   Just
play.   So just } hold me and tell me you'll be here to love me to-
say,   ex - cept

- day.   *Guitar*

To Coda ⊕   **1.**   **2.**

D.S. al Coda

$\oplus$ *Coda*

Just hold me___ and tell___ me you'll

be here to love me_____ to - day.

Just

hold me___ and tell___ me you'll be here_____ to love me to - day.

comes love

Words & Music by Sam H. Stept, Lew Brown & Charles Tobias

comes love no - thing can___ be done.
comes love, no - thing can___ be done.

2. Comes a

drum fill

Saxophone solo

26

28

That's all bro-ther if you've__ ev-er been__ in love,__

that's all__ bro-ther you know just__ what I'm think-ing of.__ Comes a night-

call me

Words & Music by Giorgio Moroder & Deborah Harry

1. Co - lour me___ your co - lour ba - by, co - lour me___ your car,___
2. Co - ver me___ with kiss - es ba - by, co - ver me___ with love.___

co - lour me a co - lour dar - ling, I
Roll me in de - sign - er sheets, I ne -

know who you are. Come up off your co -
- ver get e - nough. Emo - tions come I don't

-lour chart, I know where you're com - ing from. Call
know why, co - ver up love's a - li - bi. Call

me, in my life call me, call me a - ny, a - ny time, call me,
me in my life call me, call me a - ny time at all, call me,

a - ny place___ a - ny - where___ a - ny way.___

40

41

calling you

Words & Music by Robert Telson

Guitar Capo 3rd Fret

46

compared to what

Words & Music by Eugene McDaniels

-ing on____ with push and shove.

Pos - ses - sion is____ the mo - ti - va - tion,

hang - ing up the whole damn na - tion.

Looks like we al - ways end____ up in____ a

51

rut. _____ Try'n to make it real,_____

— but com - pared to

what?

To Coda

Slaugh - ter - house   is   kill - ing   hogs,   twis-
Pre - si - dent   he's   got   his   war,   folks__

Try'n to make it real,
Try'n to make it real,

but com - pared to
but com - pared to

1. what?
what?

Said the Go to

church on Sun - day,

sleep at night, try -

-ing to duck the wrath of God. Prea-

-chers fill-ing us_____ with pride,_____ tell-

-ing what he thinks is right. But

he must be_____ some_____ kind of stu - pid

nut,   he tries_____ to make it

real,   try   to make it   real,

yeah.   Try_____ to make it real,   real,_____

_____ yeah.   Try   to   make_____ it   real,_____

real,_____ real,_____

_____ yeah. Try to make it real,_____

_____ yeah, real,_____

_____ real_____ real real, try to make it

real.   Try   to make it real,___

yeah.   But

where's the bee,___   and where's the ho - ney?   Where's___

___ my God,___   and where's my mo - ney?   Un -

-real va - lues, crass dis - tor - tion, un -wed mo - thers need a - bor - tion. And it kind - a brings to mind oh, young kin -der. He tried

D.S. al Coda

Coda

Repeat to fade

crickets sing for anamaria

Music by Marcos Valle
Original Words by Paulo Sergio Valle
English Words by Ray Gilbert

call off the search

Words & Music by Mike Batt

2. And I won't spend my nights gaz - ing at the stars up in the

3° Instrumental

sky, won - der - ing if love will pass me by. Now

that I've found you I'll call off the search.

Now that I've found you I'll call off the

Out on my own I would nev - er have known this

2° Instrumental

68

fever

Words & Music by John Davenport & Eddie Cooley

when you kiss me, fev - er when you hold me tight.

Fev - er in the morn - ing,

fev - er all through the night.

night. Ev - 'ry - bo - dy's

got the fev - er, that is some - thing

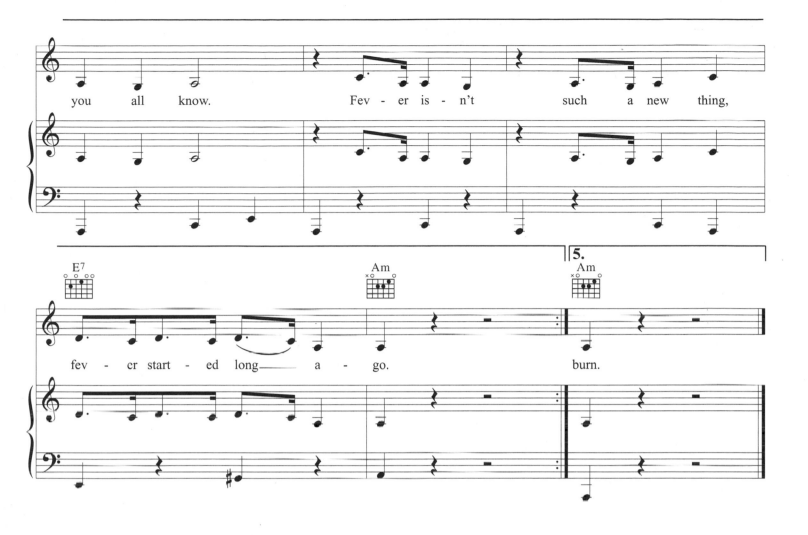

you all know. Fev - er is - n't such a new thing,

fev - er start - ed long___ a - go. burn.

Verse 3:
Romeo loved Juliet,
Juliet she felt the same,
When he put his arms around her, he said,
Julie, baby you're my flame.

CHORUS:
Thou givest fever, when we kisseth
Fever with thy flaming youth,
Fever - I'm afire
Fever, yea I burn forsooth.

Verse 4:
Captain Smith and Pocahantas
Had a very mad affair,
When her daddy tried to kill him, she said,
Daddy-o don't you dare !

CHORUS:
Give me fever, with his kisses,
Fever when he holds me tight.
Fever - I'm his Missus
Oh Daddy won't you treat him right.

Verse 5:
Now you've listened to my story
Here's the point that I have made:
Chicks were born to give you fever
Be it Farenheit or Centigrade.

CHORUS:
They give you fever when you kiss them,
Fever if you live and learn.
Fever - till you sizzle
What a lovely way to burn.

dream of life

Words & Music by Luther Henderson & Carmen McRae

ev - en the blue skies_____ a - bove had turned grey.

But now that you've come back_____ my dream of life is here to

stay._____

Those lit - tle quar - rels that tore us a - part_____

now that you're here with me, please keep it in rhyme dear

and don't stray from me. For now that you've come back my

dream of life is here to stay.

east of the sun
(and west of the moon)

Words & Music by Brooks Bowman

fine and mellow

Words & Music by Billie Holiday

My man don't love me, treats me oh so

high draped pants,__ stripes are real - ly yel - low;__

__ He wears high draped pants,__ stripes are real - ly yel -

- low. But when he starts in to love me,

he's so fine and mel - low.__ Love will

help yourself

Words & Music by Amy Winehouse, Freddy James, Larry Stock & James Hogarth

it's oh so quiet

Words & Music by Hans Lang, Bert Reisfeld & Erich Meder

bang, so what's the use of fall - ing in love.

i wish i knew how it would feel to be free

Words by Billy Taylor & Dick Dallas
Music by Billy Taylor

wish I knew how it would feel to be free. I

wish I could break all the chains hold - ing

me. I wish I could say all the things

that I should say, say 'em loud, say 'em

the nearness of you

Words by Ned Washington
Music by Hoagy Carmichael

all my_____ wild - est dreams came___ true._____

I___ need no___ soft lights to en - chant me,_____

if you_____ will on - ly grant me

so nice (summer samba)

Music by Marcos Valle
Original Words by Paulo Sergio Valle
English Words by Norman Gimbel

Some-one to hold me tight that would be ve-ry nice, some-one to love me right,
Some-one to cling to me, stay with me right or wrong, some-one to sing to me

that would be ve-ry nice. Some-one to un-der-stand each lit-tle dream in me,
some lit-tle sam-ba song. Some-one to take my heart and give his heart to me,

112

Should it be giv-en me, I could see it will be

nice.

that ole devil called love

Words & Music by Doris Fisher & Allan Roberts

well give up the fight a-gain. I know darn well he'll con-vince me that he's

right a-gain. When he sings that si-ren song,

I just got-ta tag a-long with that ole dev-il called love.

ole dev-il called love, with that ole dev-il called love.

time is a healer

Words & Music by Diane Scanlon & Greg Smith

1. I've found a pic - ture of your _____
(Verse 2 see block lyric)

smil - ing face, _____ bring - ing old _____ mem -'ries _____

that I _____ had _____ locked a - way. _____ The _____ bur - den of

an - ger _____ from _____ a heart _____ filled with pain _____

was fin - al - ly _____ lift - ed and I

smile _____ at you a - gain. Oh, _____

Verse 2:
I spoke such harsh words before our goodbye
Well I wanted to hurt you for the tears you made
You made me cry
All my hopes and dreams, well they started vanishing
Those tender hurt feelings became a dangerous thing.

Oh, if time is a healer *etc.*

love has no pride

Words & Music by Eric Kaz & Libby Titus

Fine times have gone and left my sad home
I've heard you talk said she's cra-zy to stay,

friends who once cared just walk out my door.
but this love hurts me so I don't care what you say.

Love has no pride when I call out your

name, love has no pride

125